BEAU PEEP BOOK 15

From The

DAILY STAR

©1994

Express Newspapers plc
Researched by
Mark Burgess

Published by

BOOKS

Pedigree Books Limited,
The Old Rectory,
Matford Lane, Exeter,
Devon, EX2 4PS.

under licence from
Express Newspapers plc

ISBN 1-874507-28-7
Printed in Italy

D0315985

£3.99

BEAU PEEP

EGON

THE NOMAD

MAD PIERRE

On the left, Roger Kettle strikes his "Relaxed, man-of-the-world" pose.

On the right, Andrew Christine strikes his "Get-your-hands-off-my-shoulder" pose.

Photo by Newport Studios, Fife.

THE ADVENTURES OF LEGIONNAIRE
BEAU PEEP
FROM THE STAR